ANDiDREW™

TORAH COMICS

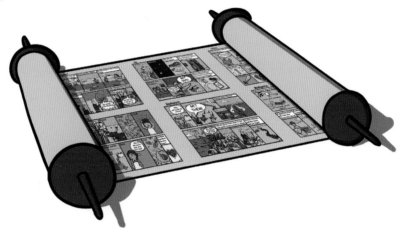

Comic Strips Summarizing the Weekly Parshah

Created by Andrew Galitzer

gefen
publishing house בית הוצאה לאור גפן
JERUSALEM • NEW YORK   Est. 1981

Fonts: Poetson One, EB Garamond, and Comic Sans

ISBN: 978-965-7801-06-2
1 3 5 7 9 8 6 4 2

Gefen Publishing House Ltd.
6 Hatzvi Street
Jerusalem 9438614,
Israel
972-2-538-0247
orders@gefenpublishing.com

Gefen Books
c/o Baker & Taylor Publisher Services
30 Amberwood Parkway
Ashland, Ohio 44805
516-593-1234
orders@gefenpublishing.com

www.gefenpublishing.com

Printed in Israel
Library of Congress Control Number: 2022904359

www.ANDiDREW.com      www.TorahComics.com

Lovingly dedicated to my supportive parents and grandparents

Barry and Jillian Galitzer
Saba Abba and Grandma Sandy Borowich
Grandpa Josh and Savta Debbie Galitzer

Thank you for your love and encouragement.

Contents

Foreword   vii

Preface   ix

Acknowledgments   xi

Bereishit

Bereishit   2

Noach   3

Lech Lecha   4

Vayera   5

Chayei Sarah   6

Toldot   7

Vayetzei   8

Vayishlach   9

Vayeshev   10

Miketz   11

Vayigash   12

Vayechi   13

Shemot

Shemot   16

Va'era   17

Bo   18

Beshalach   19

Yitro   20

Mishpatim   21

Terumah   22

Tetzaveh   23

Ki Tisa   24

Vayakhel   25

Pekudei   26

Vayikra

Vayikra   28

Tzav   28

Shemini   29

Tazria   29

Metzora   30

Acharei Mot   30

Kedoshim   31

Emor   31

Behar   32

Bechukotai   32

Bamidbar

Bamidbar   34
Naso   34
Behaalotcha   35
Shelach   35
Korach   36
Chukat   36
Balak   37
Pinchas   37
Mattot   38
Masei   38

Devarim

Devarim   40
Va'etchanan   40
Ekev   41
Re'eh   41
Shoftim   42
Ki Tetzei   42
Ki Tavo   43
Nitzavim   43
Vayelech   44

Ha'azinu   44
Vezot Haberachah 45

Chazak, Chazak,
   v'Nitchazek!   46
Glossary   47
About the Artist 48
Creating Torah Comics 49
Extras   50

Foreword

What is your earliest memory of reading biblical stories? Is it your elementary school teacher? Possibly a grandparent who read you stories? A particular book? What tools do we use to discuss the parshah with our children? How do we arouse the interest of our listeners? How do we engage them?

The Talmud tells us that when God was instructing Moshe regarding the detailed architectural plans for the Mishkan (the Tabernacle), written textual instructions were not enough. Moshe failed to understand. He had to be given a visual image – a pictorial sketch – in order to appreciate the full grandeur of the Mishkan: "According to all that I show you, the pattern of the Mishkan and the design of all its vessels.... Make according to the design which you have been shown on the mountain" (Shemot 25:9, 40). Rashbam and Ibn Ezra point to Yechezkel, who visualizes the Temple in his prophetic visions. The Rambam (Maimonides) tells us that prophecy was communicated through visual "parables" that need decoding and explaining by the spiritual virtuosity of the prophet. Again, spiritual messages are communicated via imagery and art. Sometimes pictures speak louder than words.

Text, especially in Hebrew, can be an obstacle to some children, and pictorial stories can open up entire worlds. Some people are simply visual learners. How about children who are not yet reading? For others, images are a means of connecting to a side of the story that they wouldn't appreciate through mere words; the pictures bring the words to life. It is for this reason that it is my pleasure and honor to welcome Andrew Galitzer's book *Torah Comics*, which has been years in the making.

Andrew, with whom I have studied at Yeshivat Eretz Hatzvi, is a talented artist and a magnificent cartoonist. He is also a wonderful teacher who can connect with young and old alike. He brings a sincerity, a conscientiousness, and a deep commitment to all he does. I have seen many of his parshah comics, and they are a fabulous resource – enjoyable for kids and a superb teaching tool for adults – as he summarizes the major topics and themes of the *parshat hashavua* and brings them alive in cartoon format. I can see parents using the images as a way of transmitting the content of our Torah, as well as using the pictures as the basis for discussion around the parshah. Andrew has put in hours of thought and research into his parshah comics. I highly recommend this book.

Bivrachah
Rabbi Alex Israel
Yeshivat Eretz Hatzvi

Preface

When I was in elementary school, the parshah didn't excite me. I enjoyed picture books, so I didn't really enjoy the pictureless parshah-packets my teachers distributed. Once I was in sixth grade, I developed my artistic abilities and drew during every class. However, Rabbi Allen Saks, my Gemara (Talmud) teacher would only let me draw something if it related to Judaic studies. From then on, I drew Torah comics in each of his classes. Since then, I have been redrawing the comics every year, each cycle of the Torah becoming more professional as my skills have improved, starting off with just pencils and eventually graduating to a drawing tablet. After completing over three cycles of the Torah, I am finally ready to publish my comics and share them with the world.

Each parshah is summarized in one or two comic strips, to make it easy to understand. In order to keep them bite-sized, I filtered the stories to focus on the main ideas and storyline. I tried my best to include as much as I could in each comic, yet sadly had to exclude some details. In addition, I chose not to include any Midrashim (rabbinic commentary), since there are so many that conflict, and I did not think it was my place to decide which to incorporate into the comics. The comics therefore focus on the peshat (the literal understanding of the text). I made the comics vague when the Torah is vague – for example, not naming Avraham's servant Eliezer in Chayei Sarah. For the reader's ease, all frames of mitzvot have a background of light purple or green. Lastly, there are a few jokes in the comics to keep the reader entertained. To differentiate between the jokes and the Torah content, all jokes are italicized. I did not add a joke for every parshah, because I wanted to keep this an educational tool and not make light of the Torah.

While I started making the comics seven years ago for my personal enjoyment, I am proud to now make the comics to educate kids of all ages and backgrounds on the weekly parshah. Since 2018, the comics have been sent to shuls, schools, and families around the world for children to learn and enjoy. There are a few ways to use the comics. Younger children can be introduced to the Torah through them. Older children who are familiar with the parashah can read them to review what they learned and bring the story to life. Teens as well as adults can reference them as they read through the parshah to pick up on details they may have overlooked.

A challenge that comes up in creating English Torah comics is the terminology. For example, should it be called *Torah Comics*? *Old Testament Comics*? *Pentateuch Comics*? Should names be based on English conventions, such as Abraham, Isaac, and Jacob? Or transliterated based on the Hebrew text, such as Avraham, Yitzchak, and Yaakov? Should the Jews be called Jews? Hebrews? Israelites? Bnei Yisrael?

Each of these terms has its own unique value and validity. For this first edition of the *Torah Comics*, I decided to use the transliterated terms that I was familiar with throughout my childhood. I use the term *Jews* in the comics because it has become a widely accepted and popular term in the modern world to refer to people of our religion. By the same token, I refer to the Promised Land as Israel instead of Canaan. On a similar note, I chose to give each Jewish male a kippah (yarmulke/head covering), even though the Avot (forefathers) did not wear them. My goal is for the reader to associate the Jews and Israel of today with their counterparts in the Torah.

For the reader's ease, there is a glossary of some words and their meanings at the end of the book.

Andrew Galitzer

Acknowledgments

Gratitude is an important value that my parents and grandparents taught me. My bar mitzvah speech, which I worked on with my Savta, was centered around *bikkurim* (giving of the first fruits to Hashem to show *hakarat hatov* [gratitude]). I feel blessed to have so many people to thank for helping me accomplish my dream of publishing this book.

First of all, I can't thank my parents enough for the strong Jewish foundation they instilled within me. Not only did they give me an encompassing Jewish education, they also were – and continue to be – my role models. I hope to continue to bring them and my grandparents *nachat* (enjoyment) for many years to come. No words can describe how much I value their love and support. Family movie nights were often interrupted by the glow of my laptop as I worked on that week's parshah comic. Nevertheless, my parents and my siblings, Ashley and Steven, rarely complained. They always offered to help me edit the comics, never restraining themselves from rejecting the puns and dad jokes.

I am attached to each drawing and word and was nervous about going through the editing process. My first-draft editors' suggestions and ideas, especially those from Danny Verbov and Shira Greenspan, greatly impressed me. Shira, your creativity is truly astounding; I particularly loved your idea of having one color throughout the comics for each of the twelve tribes. In addition, thank you to Rabbi Alex Israel, Rabbi Zvi Grumet, Rabbi Joshua Amaru, Morah Hadassah Smolarcik, and Ms. Kyla Crowther for your advice. Each of you has taught me so much.

How do I begin to thank Avi Frier? I don't even know what I should call you. My previous employer? Business advisor? Marketing agent? Youth director? Humor consultant? We have been through a lot together. Thank you for always pushing me to excel in business and beyond. I am appreciative to my lawyer, Michael Chesal, for helping me protect my comics under copyright and trademark my brand, ANDiDREW™.

I would also like to recognize and show appreciation to all of my teachers for providing me with a thorough Jewish education. This all started with Rabbi Allen Saks allowing me to draw something related to the parshah during class in sixth grade and continued after high school. I was fortunate to grow up in Hollywood, Florida, and to be a part of Young Israel, Brauser Maimonides, Katz Hillel Day School, and Katz Yeshiva High School. Each of these remarkable institutions greatly fostered my religious growth and made me who I am today. After high school, I was honored to attend Yeshivat Eretz Hatzvi, which reinforced my connection to Judaism and made me feel at home in Israel. In addition, I am thankful for Bnei Akiva and the incredible leadership opportunities and experiential education they provided for me. I was fortunate to attend weekly programs and to teach art at Camp Stone and Moshava Alevy. These educational influences have profoundly impacted me, and I am grateful for all of these experiences.

Receiving Ilan Greenfield's email that Gefen Publishing House would publish my book was a moment I will never forget. Seeing the whole team's enthusiasm when I visited their office in Jerusalem made me proud to publish with Gefen. I am grateful to my publisher Ilan Greenfield, project manager Daphne Abrahams, my editor Kezia Raffel Pride, and the whole team for working with me to make my eight-year project a success.

Lastly, this book would not have been possible without the generous contributions of Danny and Debby Aqua, Alex and Chava Mann, Matthew and Nicola Tiller, Rabbi Akiva and Dr. Rachel Wolk, and my grandparents. I can't thank you enough for enabling me to fulfill my dream of publishing this book.

Bereishit
Noach
Lech Lecha
Vayera

Chayei Sarah
Toldot
Vayetzei
Vayishlach

Vayeshev
Miketz
Vayigash
Vayechi

Bereishit

Noach

Andrew Galitzer

Lech Lecha

Vayera

Chayei Sarah

Toldot

Vayetzei

Vayishlach

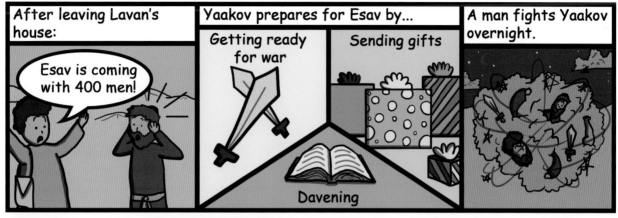

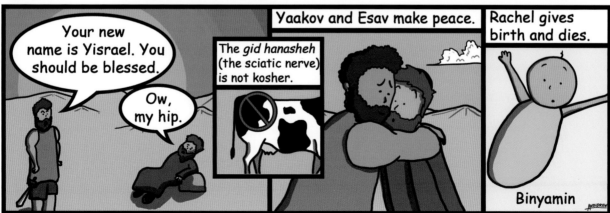

Vayeshev

Miketz

Vayigash

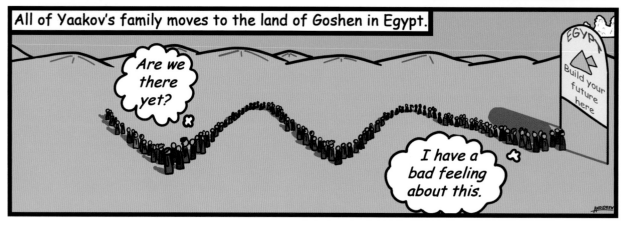

Vayechi

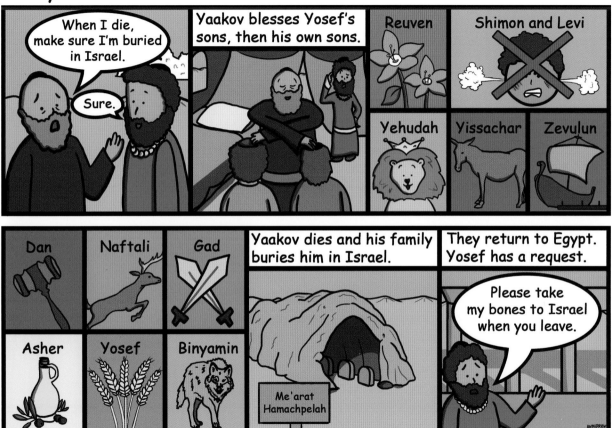

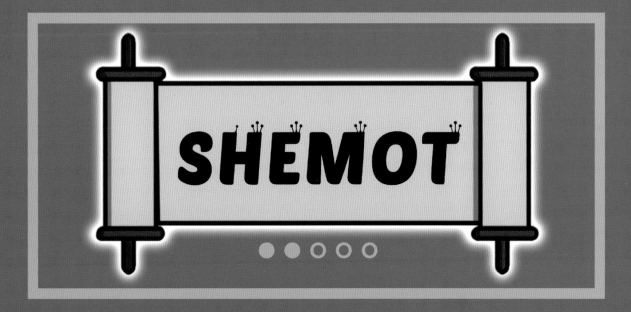

SHEMOT

Shemot
Va'era
Bo
Beshalach

Yitro
Mishpatim
Terumah
Tetzaveh

Ki Tisa
Vayakhel
Pekudei

Shemot

Va'era

17

Andrew Galitzer

Bo

18

Beshalach

Yitro

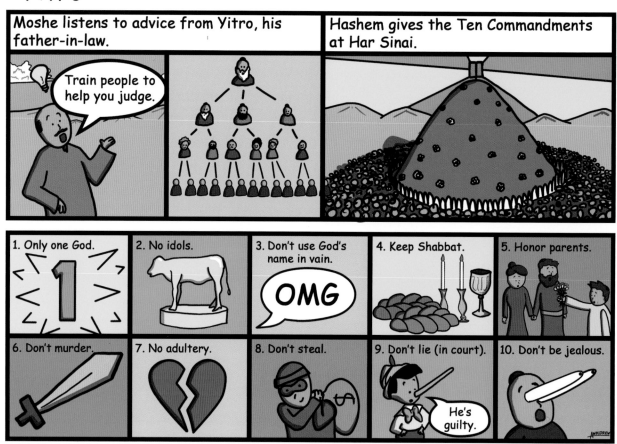

Mishpatim

21

Terumah

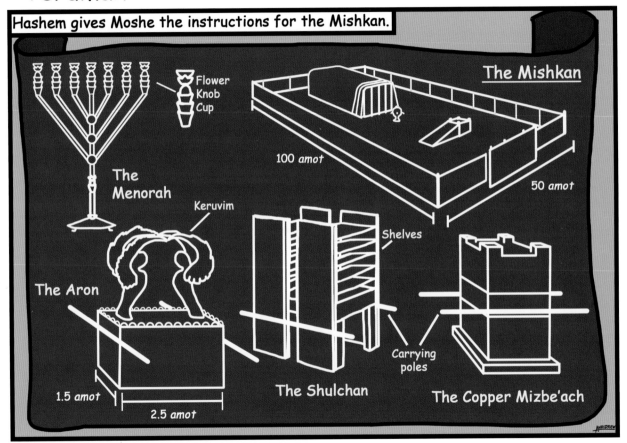

Tetzaveh

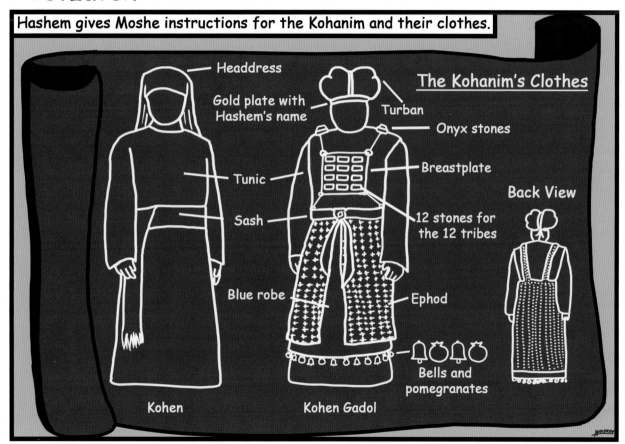

Ki Tisa

Vayakhel

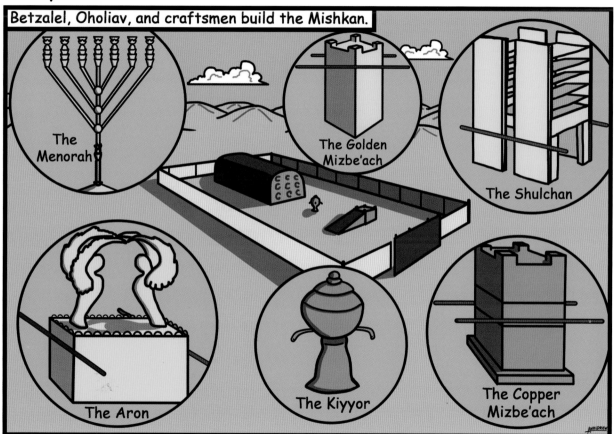

Pekudei

The Jews make the Kohanim's clothes.

Kohen

Kohen Gadol

Vayikra   Metzora   Behar

Tzav   Acharei Mot   Bechukotai

Shemini   Kedoshim

Tazria   Emor

Vayikra

Tzav

Shemini

Tazria

Metzora

Acharei Mot

Kedoshim

Emor

Behar

Bechukotai

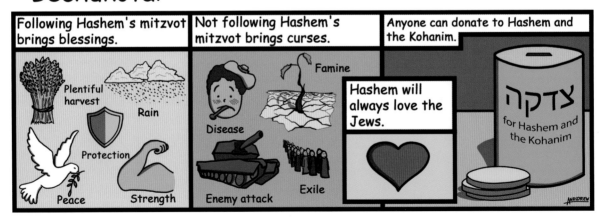

Bamidbar
Naso
Behaalotcha
Shelach

Korach
Chukat
Balak
Pinchas

Mattot
Masei

Bamidbar

Naso

Behaalotcha

Shelach

35

Andrew Galitzer

Korach

Chukat

Balak

Pinchas

Andrew Galitzer

Mattot

Masei

38

Devarim   Shoftim   Vayelech
Va'etchanan   Ki Tetzei   Ha'azinu
Ekev   Ki Tavo   Vezot Haberachah
Re'eh   Nitzavim

Devarim

Va'etchanan

Ekev

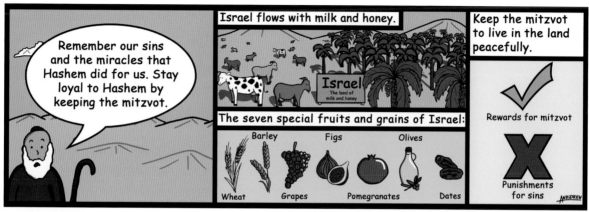

Re'eh

Shoftim

Ki Teitzei

Ki Tavo

Nitzavim

Vayelech

Ha'azinu

Vezot Haberachah

Chazak, Chazak, v'Nitchazek!

It is so exciting and satisfying when you finish something, especially when you finish a cycle of the Torah. Every year on Simchat Torah, we celebrate the completion of reading the Torah. Immediately after we finish Vezot Haberachah, we start again from Bereishit. We see a similar tradition with learning Gemara (Talmud): there is a custom to start a new *masechta* (tractate) immediately after completing one. In Judaism, there is always more to learn, and we can always start learning something new.

However, we don't start something "new" after finishing the Torah. We roll back the scroll and start right back again from the beginning. The Torah is so deep that there is always something new to discover. The challenge is for us to make it new and exciting each year. Luckily, there are countless classic and modern commentaries on the Torah, and each year you can read a new one.

My year in yeshiva opened my eyes to how remarkably deep the Torah is and that there is no end to how much someone can learn. My rabbis have been studying Tanach for over forty years, and they continue to discover new ideas and write books on their finds. It is truly quite inspiring: after over three thousand years of people studying the Torah, more is still being uncovered. Even with the completion of this Torah comic book – after three years of finished cycles and revisions – I know I have far more to learn and will have much to improve in future editions.

Hopefully, we will all have the merit to finish many more books, but never "finish" learning. We should continue to be impacted by the lessons we learned and continue to learn. I hope that after finishing this book, you are more familiar with the Torah and feel prepared to delve deeper into your Torah learning.

חזק חזק ונתחזק!

Glossary

Below are words used in the comics that may be unfamiliar to you, listed in the order in which they appear.

BEREISHIT
שבת = Shabbat = Sabbath
Chavah = Eve
Gan Eden = Garden of Eden
Noach = Noah
Hashem = God
Migdal Bavel = Tower of Babel
Avraham = Abraham
Israel = Land of Israel/Canaan
brit milah = ritual circumcision
Yitzchak = Isaac
Me'arat Hamachpelah = Double Cave (of the Patriarchs)
Rivkah = Rebecca
Esav = Esau
Yaakov = Jacob
Lavan = Laban
Yehudah = Judah
Yosef = Joseph
Yisrael = Israel
gid hanesheh = sciatic nerve

SHEMOT
Paroh = Pharaoh
Moshe = Moses

Aharon = Aaron
Korban Pesach – Passover sacrifice
mitzvot = commandments
mon = manna
Amalek = an evil nation descended from Esav
Yitro = Jethro
Har Sinai = Mount Sinai
Mishkan = Tabernacle
Aron = Ark
amot = plural of *amah*, a unit of measurement
Keruvim = Cherubs
Shulchan = Table
Mizbe'ach = Altar
Kohanim = Priests
Kohen = Priest
Kohen Gadol = High Priest
Luchot = Tablets
Kiyyor = Washing Station

VAYIKRA
korbanot = plural of *korban*
korban = sacrifice
lashon hara = evil speech

tzaraat = a spiritual affliction equated with leprosy
mikveh = ritual bath
צדקה = tzedakah = charity
Pesach = Passover
Shemittah = Sabbatical year
Yovel = Jubilee year

BAMIDBAR
Leviim = Levites
Nazir = Nazirite
hafrashat challah = bread offering
tzitzit = ritual fringes
Pinchas = Phinehas
Tzelofchad = Zelophehad
Yehoshua = Joshua

DEVARIM
Shema = central prayer of Judaism
tefillin = phylacteries
mezuzot = small scrolls for doorposts
Beit Hamikdash = Temple

About the Artist

Award-winning artist Andrew Galitzer is a young Orthodox Jew, passionate about uniting Judaism and art with his Torah comics. He attended Jewish schools all his life, reinforcing his religious identity. Following Katz Yeshiva High School, he attended Yeshivat Eretz HaTzvi in Israel to study Torah and mitzvot on a deeper level. Currently an undergraduate at Drexel University, Andrew runs biweekly parshah classes as the education chair of the Orthodox community on campus.

Throughout his years of education, Andrew developed his personal drawing style. His artwork has won awards from the Boca Raton Fine Art Show, Teach Coalition, Chidon Hatanach, the Combat Anti-Semitism Movement, and the Jewish Museum of Florida. He created the name ANDiDREW™, as in "I went to Israel *and I drew,*" which evolved into a globally recognized resource for Jewish educational materials. Andrew expanded his business to include Zoom drawing classes and Torah Comics Workshops to fulfill the need for virtual activities in 2020. Andrew pitched this idea to win first place in the Baiada Institute Student Pitch Competition.

Today, ANDiDREW™ is a popular cartooning studio that inspires thousands of Jewish artists of all ages. Andrew hopes to continue to impact Jewish communities around the world and share his love for Judaism and art.

© Baila Shatzkes

Creating Torah Comics

While Andrew used to make comics with just paper and pencil in sixth grade, he now uses Photoshop on a MacBook with a Wacom drawing tablet to make them professionally.

Andrew first reads through the parshah and drafts comic ideas on paper. He then creates a Photoshop file and designs the comic boxes, bubbles, and text. He then uses his drawing tablet to roughly sketch the comic idea in red. On a new layer, he draws the comic using the sketch as a guide. With the drawing completed, Andrew fills it with color. Finally, to complete the comic, he draws shadows using a low opacity layer.

Do you want to make your own comics? Check out the next page or visit www.TorahComics.com for workshops.

Comic Coloring Page

Visit www.TorahComics.com/readers for free comics, workshops and resources.

Bereishit

Name:

Free Comic Workshop Boxes

Visit www.TorahComics.com/readers for free comics, workshops and resources.

Shemot

Name:

Create Your Own Torah Comics!

Follow easy step-by-step instructions to create your very own Torah comics!

Try it for **FREE!**

Create your own Torah comics with the boxes on page 51 and the video at TorahComics.com/readers.

www.TorahComics.com/readers